Feilhauer / Ehrhardt (Hrsg.)
Englisch lernen mit neuen Witzen

D0582385

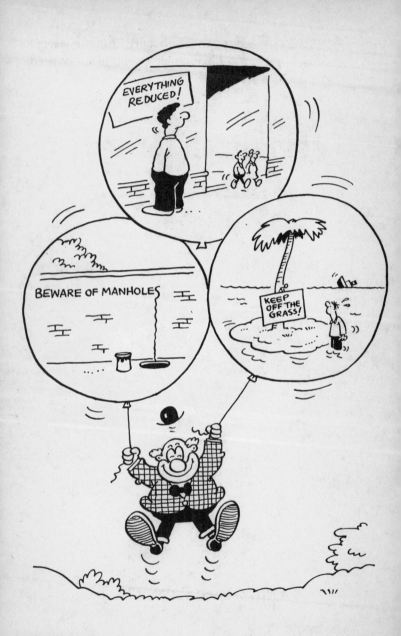

Angelika Feilhauer / Cornell Ehrhardt
(Hrsg.)

Englisch lernen mit neuen Witzen

Otto Maier Ravensburg

Originalausgabe
als Ravensburger Taschenbuch Band 1712
© 1989 Ravensburger Buchverlag Otto Maier GmbH

Umschlagillustration: Erhard Dietl

Alle Rechte vorbehalten durch
Ravensburger Buchverlag Otto Maier GmbH
Gesamtherstellung: Ebner Ulm
Printed in Germany

5 4 3   93 92 91

ISBN 3-473-51712-7

Contents

Lachen kann man immer ...

... lernen auch - nur macht das meistens lange nicht so viel Spaß. Wenn du aber dieses Buch liest, kannst du lachen *und* etwas lernen, und zwar Englisch, so wie es im täglichen Leben gesprochen wird!

Vielleicht kennst du schon unser erstes Buch "Englisch lernen mit Witzen", das wir nach sprachlichen und grammatikalischen Besonderheiten gegliedert hatten. Diesmal ist nun nach Alltagssituationen unterteilt worden. So gibt es beispielsweise Kapitel wie "In der Schule", "Auf dem Lande" oder "Beim Arzt".

Sicher wird dir auffallen, daß dieses Buch eine Reihe längerer Texte enthält. Es sind Meldungen aus Zeitungen - nicht etwa Witzgeschichten, sondern wahre Begebenheiten! Wir fanden sie unglaublich komisch und oft viel witziger als jeden noch so gelungenen "erfundenen" Witz.

Die Auswahl der Texte wurde so getroffen, daß man sie mit Englischkenntnissen der Mittelstufe verstehen kann. Besonders schwierige Wörter werden jedoch wieder in einer Vokabelliste am Ende des Buches erklärt. Sie enthält auch die übliche Lautschrift.

Und ganz bestimmt entdeckst du beim Lesen dieses Buches vieles wieder, was du bereits im Englischunterricht gelernt hast - aber eben mal ganz anders.

Also dann, viel Spaß!

The happiest days of your life

"Now I want you to imagine that my hat is Mars and this apple is the moon," said the science teacher. "Notice how small the moon is compared to the planet. Any questions?"

"Yes, sir," said Alec. "Is Mars inhabited?"

Paul was more than angry when the teacher asked him to play the innkeeper in the school nativity play. He had set his heart on playing Joseph.

On the night of the play, Mary and Joseph came on the stage, stopped at the inn and asked Paul if there was any room. This was the moment Paul had been waiting for.

"Of course! There's plenty. And would you like me to phone the midwife for your wife?"

The history teacher was the dullest teacher in school. One day John was bored to tears, and he looked like it.

"Do you have trouble hearing me, John?" the teacher asked.

"No, sir! I have trouble listening to you."

English teacher: "I'm sure if William Shakespeare were with us today we'd still regard him as an exceptional man."

Pupil: "Yes, sir. Especially as he'd be well over four hundred and twenty years old."

Teacher: "Tommy, your hands are very dirty. What would you say if I came to school with dirty hands?"
Tommy: "I'd be too polite to mention it."

Teacher: "If we breathe oxygen in the daytime, what do we breathe at night?"
Johnny: "Nitrogen."

The school inspector wanted to demonstrate to the children that if they spotted someone making a mistake they should not be afraid to point it out. So he asked someone to call out a number.
"21!"
The inspector wrote down 12. But no one pointed out the error.
"Another number?"
"46!"
He wrote down 64. Still no response.
"One more!"
"33!" cried Alec. "And let's see how he messes up that one," he whispered to his neighbour.

Kind old gentleman: "How do you like going to school, Peter?"
Peter: "I like going all right, and I like coming home, too. But I can't stand staying there in between."

Teacher: "Why can't you answer any of the questions?"
Pupil: "So that I have a reason for coming to school. If I could answer them all what would be the point of being in your class?"

Teacher: "Can anyone tell me what Picasso and Braque have in common?"
Simon: "They are both dead, sir."

Teacher: "Where are you from?"
New pupil: "Devon, Miss."
Teacher: "Which part?"
New pupil: "All of me, Miss."

When Bud, an American boy, came to school, the games master asked Alec to explain the rules of cricket to him. "Well," said Alec, "there are two sides, one out in the field and one in the pavilion. Each man in the side that's in goes out and when he's out he comes in and the next man goes in until he's out. When they're all out, the side that's been out comes in and the side that's been in goes out and tries to get the players coming in, out. When both sides have been in and out, including the not-outs, that's the end of the game."
"Thanks", said Bud. "I'll stick to baseball."

A teacher was talking to a new boy in her class.

Teacher: "What's your name?"

Boy: "Let's see...Happy birthday to you, happy birthday to you, happy birthday dear Brian ... it's Brian, Miss!"

RE teacher: "Who do you suppose sits at God's right hand?"

Pupil: "Mrs God, sir?"

Biology teacher: "What's the opposite of evergreen?"

Sarah: "Never green?"

"Why haven't you done your homework? It was simple!" said the arithmetic teacher. "If a man walks ten miles in five hours, how long will it take him to walk twenty miles?"

"I still don't know, Miss. Dad's not back yet."

"Where is the English Channel?" asked the geography teacher.

"Don't ask me, sir," said the little girl. "We only get BBC 1 on our television."

Teacher: "No Johnny! BC does not mean Before Calculators."

Johnny: "Sorry, sir."

Teacher: "What do you think AD means?"

Johnny: "After Dinner?"

Maths teacher: "John! If tomatoes were 80p a pound and you had £ 2.40, how many would you buy?"
John: "None, sir. If I had £ 2.40, I'd go to the pictures."

The teacher went to call at Susie's house. "I'd like to see your mother," she said when Susie opened the door.
"She ain't here," Susie answered.
"Oh Susie! Where's your grammar!" the teacher said.
"She ain't here neither," said Susie.

Svenda Norselander, a girl from Lapland, came to our school for a term.
"We have geography lessons first," said the teacher.
"I am not knowing the geography," said Svenda.
"How about history?"
"I am not knowing the history."
"Domestic science?"
"What is this domestic science?"
"Chemistry? Physics? Botany?"
"I know not what these things are."
"What do you know?" asked the teacher trying to keep her temper.
"I am knowing how to breed the reindeer."
That was the last straw.
"We don't need to breed rain here!" cried the teacher. "We have enough already. And don't be so familiar with me on your first day at school."

"Can we go home now, Miss?" asked Alec.
"No you can't. The bell hasn't gone yet."
"But Miss! Only yesterday you told us not to leave everything to the last minute."

Teacher: "Claire! Cover your mouth with your hand when you yawn."
Claire: "What! And get my fingers bitten?"

Geography teacher: "What's the capital of Spain?"
William: "All the money they get from tourism."

At a very trendy school where parents were constantly being divorced a little boy turned to another and asked, "How do you like your new father?"
"Oh, he's very nice," said the lad.
"Yes, isn't he? We had him two years ago."

"Are you good at maths, Bill?" asked the new teacher.
"Well. Yes and no, sir."
"What do you mean 'yes and no'?"
"Yes, sir. I'm no good at maths."

What's the difference between a boring teacher and a boring book?
You can shut the book up.

"How can you make so many mistakes in one day?" Alec's teacher asked him.
"I get up very early and go to bed late, sir."

"Susan, what's a synonym?"
"It's a word I can't spell that means the same as one I can."

15

The art teacher was discussing 'The Holy Family' by Michelangelo.

"Please, sir?" asked Mary. "Why wasn't Jesus born in a proper bed?"

"Because there was no room at the inn, and anyway, his parents were very poor."

"They can't have been that poor if they could afford to have themselves painted by Michelangelo."

"If it wasn't for rain," the science master droned on, "there would be nothing growing – no trees, flowers, grass ..."

"But why does it rain on the pavement?" asked Arthur.

"I hope you're not one of those boys who sits and watches the school clock," said the headmaster to a new boy.

"No, sir. I've got a digital watch that bleeps at half past one."

"I'm sorry that I won't be teaching you next term when you go to senior school," said Sue's primary school teacher.

"So am I, Miss. It's a pity you don't know enough to work there."

Art teacher: "This slide shows a famous sculpture by Rodin, called 'The Thinker'. Can anyone suggest what he's thinking about?"

Anne: "He's probably trying to remember where he left his clothes!"

16

English teacher: "What is the future of 'He drinks'?"
Nick: "He will be drunk."

"Can anyone tell me where the Virgin Islands are?" the geography teacher asked.
"I'm not exactly sure, Miss," said Tim. "But I bet they're some distance from the Isle of Man."

Alec: "How did I get on in my spelling test?"
Teacher: "There was an enormous improvement today, Alec. You spelt your name correctly."

"Ann, I can hear you talking to Billy," said the teacher.
"Has no one ever told you it's rude to listen to other people's conversations, Miss?"

Why did the soccer teacher give his team lighters?
Because they kept losing all their matches.

Why did the maths teacher take a ruler to bed with him?
He wanted to see how long he would sleep.

Alec's voice was so out of tune that when he sang, the music teacher put his hands over his ears.
"Sorry, sir," said Alec. "I've got a frog in my throat."
"Well let's hear it sing then. It can't be worse than you."

Science teacher: "Did you wash your neck this morning?"
Harry: "Yes, sir!"
Teacher (taking some cotton wool, dipping it in surgical spirit and rubbing it round Harry's neck): "What's this then?"
Harry: "Some dirt only comes off with dry cleaning."

"I want to know how you broke the classroom window. The truth now." The English master was furious with John.
"Well, I was cleaning my catapult and it sort of went off."

Teachers nowadays specialize so much that they know more and more about less and less until they know everything about nothing!

That's what friends are for

The proud mother was showing off her new baby to her friend.

"Doesn't he look just like his father?" asked the mother.

"Yes," replied the friend. "But I shouldn't worry too much – he'll probably change for the better as he gets older."

Elizabeth: "You'll never guess what! Mrs Merryweather is expecting her sixth baby."

Friend: "Someone had better warn her!"

Elizabeth: "Warn her about what?"

Friend: "I read somewhere that every sixth child born is Chinese."

Clarissa: "Do you remember our holiday together last year?"

Jane: "Yes, of course! How could I ever forget Greece?"

Clarissa: "Do you remember, then, that boyfriend I had?"

Jane: "Which one?"

Clarissa: "The one I said life wasn't worth living without."

Jane: "Well?"

Clarissa: "I've forgotten his name."

Two little boys were looking out of the window when they saw a lorry drive past loaded with turf.
"That's what I shall do when I'm rich," said one of the little boys. "I'll send my grass away to be cut, too."

I never forget a face, but in your case I'll make an exception.

One autumn evening Bill and Will went out collecting conkers. They collected a huge bag, and decided to go and share them out in the graveyard. Just as they went in, two conkers rolled out of the bag. "We'll get those later," said Bill, "let's go and share out the others first."
As they were sharing them out a little girl walked across the graveyard taking a short cut home, for it was getting dark. To her horror she heard voices, "One for you, one for me, one for you …" She flew to the gate in a terrible state and bumped straight into a policeman.
"What's the matter, little girl?" he asked, for she was shivering with fear.
"Oh," she said, "there are ghosts in the graveyard and they're sharing out the dead bodies. Listen." They both stood still, and a voice came out to them on the night air, "One for you, one for me, and we mustn't forget those two by the gate."

Paddy and Mick were watching a John Wayne film on television. In one scene John Wayne was riding furiously towards a cliff.
"I bet you £ 10 that he falls over the cliff," said Paddy.
"Done," said Mick.
John Wayne rode straight over the cliff.

As Mick handed over his £ 10, Paddy said, "I feel a bit guilty about this. I've seen the film before."
"So have I," said Mick, "but I didn't think he'd be fool enough to make the same mistake twice."

Tracey: "Why's your shirt so wet?"
Robert: "The label says 'Wash and wear'."

When Peter called on his friend Roger (who was something of a miser) he found him carefully stripping the wallpaper.
"Are you re-decorating?" asked Peter.
"Of course not!" replied Roger. "I'm moving."

Simple Simon took a friend driving in the mountains. After a while the friend said, "Every time you go round one of those sharp curves, I get frightened."
"Then why don't you do what I do?" Simple Simon answered. "Close your eyes."

"I've just come back from the beauty salon."
"Pity it was closed."

Samantha: "Why are you moaning? You've just been given a huge diamond ring. Anyone else would be absolutely happy."
Sally: "But the ring comes with the terrible curse of the Hyde-Whippenbrakes."
Samantha: "Oh – and what is the curse?"
Sally: "With the ring comes Clyde Hyde-Whippenbrake."

"A funny thing happened to my mother in Glasgow."
"Oh, really? I thought you were born in Liverpool."

Friend: "I can lie in bed and watch the sun rise."
Bobby: "So what? I can sit on a stool and watch the kitchen sink!"

Friend: "Girls fall in love with me at first sight."
Joe: "I know, it's when they take a second look that they can't stand you!"

"I feel sorry for your poor little mind, all alone in that great big head!"

Sarah: "There's no point in telling you a joke with a double meaning."
Friend: "Why not?"
Sarah: "You won't get either of them."

"Let's have an agreement: if you don't say anything, I won't listen."

"Men say I'm one in a million."
"Thank heavens."

George: "Randy has a mechanical mind."
Robert: "But some of the screws are loose."

"He's a bit dull till you get to know him. After that he's a real bore!"

Peter: "You have to believe in Father Christmas."
Friend: "Why?"
Peter: "Otherwise, we're all being good for no reason!"

"Jerry's father looks pretty old."
"That's an understatement. When he was a boy history was probably called Current Events!"

What were the Chicago gangster's last words?
"Who put that violin in my violin case?"

Rosalind: "Do you think I'll lose my looks as I get older?"
Mary: "With a bit of luck, yes."

Simple Simon: "I wonder how long someone can live without a brain?"
Brighter Bertie: "How old are you?"

Silly Sue: "We bumped into some old friends last week."
Smart Alec: "Your brother was driving again, was he?"

A man coughed violently, and his false teeth shot across the room and crashed against the wall. "Oh, dear," he said, "whatever shall I do? I can't afford a new set."
"Don't worry," said his friend. "I'll get a pair from my brother for you."
The next day the friend came back with the teeth, which fitted perfectly. "This is wonderful," said the man. "Your brother must be a very good dentist."
"Oh, he's not a dentist," replied his friend. "He's an undertaker."

First burglar: "Quick! It's the police! Jump out of the window!"
Second burglar: "But we're on the thirteenth floor!"
First burglar: "This is no time to be superstitious."

Billy: "I was at the zoo last summer."
Joe: "Which cage were you in?"

English boy: "My grandfather was touched on the shoulder by Queen Victoria, and that made him a knight."
American boy: "That's nothing! My grandfather was touched on the head with a tomahawk by an Apache and that made him an angel."

Annie: "Why is your dog looking at me like that?"
Danny: "Possibly because you're eating out of his bowl."

Businessman: "I bought a barometer in Tokyo."
Unimpressed friend: "Who wants to know if it's raining in Japan?"

Nick: "Can you tell me the way to Bath?"
Rick: "I use soap and water, personally."

Amy: "Johnny keeps telling me that he's going to marry the most beautiful girl in the world."
Sandra: "Oh, what a shame! And you've been engaged for such a long time!"

Jim: "How do you do?"
Jack: "Do what?"
Jim: "I mean, how do you find yourself?"
Jack: "I'm never lost."
Jim: "What I mean is, how do you feel?"
Jack: "With my fingers, of course. Do stop bothering me with all these silly questions!"

Mr Able: "I've been shopping for my wife's birthday present."
Mr Cable: "What did you get her?"
Mr Able: "A bottle of expensive toilet water. It cost £ 20."
Mr Cable: "£ 20! Why didn't you come to my house – you could have had some of ours for free!"

Mrs Able: "I'd love you to stay the night, but I'm afraid you'll have to make your own bed."
Mrs Cable: "Oh, that's all right, I don't mind at all."
Mrs Able: "Right. Here's a hammer, a saw, and some nails. The wood's in the garage."

Paul: "Guess what happened after I saw you yesterday and you said, 'Cheer up, things could be worse'?"
Bob: "What happened?"
Paul: "Things got worse."

Jack: "What happened to that dumb blonde Johnny used to go out with?"
Jill: "I dyed my hair."

Susie: "Do you think I'm a fool?"
Elizabeth: "No. But what's my opinion against thousands of others?"

Mrs Brown: "Go on, then, tell me some more gossip about Jack and Jill."
Mrs Sanders: "I can't. I've already told you more than I heard myself."

A snobbish woman was showing a friend round her new house.
"It's very lovely," her friend admitted, "but what you need in this big room is a chandelier."
"I know, my dear," said her hostess, "but nobody in the family plays one."

Shopping is fun

Simple Simon was looking at some new cars in London. He seemed to like one sports car very much. "Is it a good fast car?" he asked the salesman.

"Fast!" said the salesman. "If you got that car now, you'd be in Aberdeen by three o'clock tomorrow morning. Do you want to buy it?"

"I'll think about it", Simple Simon said, and he went home. The next day he was back. "I don't want that car," he told the salesman. "All night long I stayed awake thinking, and I couldn't think of a single reason why I'd want to be in Aberdeen at three o'clock in the morning."

Mrs Bloggins: "I'd like some nuts, please."
Shop assistant: "Certainly, madam. What sort?"
Mrs Bloggins: "Cashew."
Shop assistant: "Bless you! Now what nuts would you like, madam?"

Oxford Street was bursting at the seams and Dawn and Mrs Witt pushed their way through the crowds.

"Hey!" came a voice. "Who d'you think you're pushing?"

"I don't know," screamed Dawn. "What's your name?"

"Who shall I ask for?" the customer said.
"My name is Shakespeare, sir."

"Oh, really? May I ask what your Christian name is?"
"William, sir."
"Indeed! That is a well-known name."
"Well, I've been here for ten years, sir, so people ought to know me now."

Customer: "Can I have half a pound of mixed nuts, please?"
Shop assistant: "Certainly, madam."
Customer: "And please make sure there aren't too many coconuts."

Read in the papers
In 1957 Ford produced a real winner – the Edsel. One of the largest and most luxurious cars ever made, it was built at a time when people were turning more and more to economical cars. As *Time* magazine said: "It was a classic case of the wrong car for the wrong market at the wrong time."
In addition to this, more than half the models sold were found to have some or all of the following defects: doors that wouldn't close, bonnets and boots that wouldn't open, batteries that went flat, horns that wouldn't work, hubcaps that dropped off, brakes that failed, paint that peeled and push buttons which were impossible to push.
No wonder that the Edsel's sales graph was compared by a journalist to an extremely dangerous ski-slope. Even car thieves seemed to keep clear. As far as the writer knew, there was only ever one case reported of an Edsel being stolen.

It was the most luxurious greengrocer's he had ever seen, but he could only gasp when he was charged ninety pence for a pound of apples.

He gave the girl a one pound coin and walked out of the shop.

"You've forgotten your change, sir," she said, going after him with ten pence.

"Keep it," he said weakly. "On my way in I stepped on a grape."

Money isn't everything – usually, it isn't even enough!

"I need to go to the off-licence. I'm getting a bottle of whiskey for my husband."

"Seems like a good swop..."

Woman: "Have you got a sheep's head?"
Butcher: "No, madam, it's the way I part my hair."

Dawn was doing the shopping with her mother. A vicar approached wearing ordinary clothes.
"Good morning Vicar!" said Mother.
"How do you know he's a vicar?" asked Dawn.
"I should know him," replied Mother, "he's the man that married me."
"In that case," said Dawn, "who's the man who hangs around our house that I call 'Father'?"

John was at a cocktail party where he was boasting about his latest sales success. "And do you know how much I sold?" he asked his bored victim.

"Probably about half," replied the bored fellow.

"Half? What do you mean by half?" asked John.

"Half of what you'll tell me you sold."

The apprentice had been left in charge of the chemist's shop during the lunch-hour, and when the chemist returned, he asked if there had been any customers.

"Just one," said the apprentice, "a fellow with a terrible cough, so I gave him a dose of castor oil."

"You what?" demanded the chemist. "Castor oil isn't a remedy for a cough!"

The apprentice looked puzzled. "Well, it seems to have worked," he said. "That's him over there hanging on that lamppost, and he hasn't dared cough in over half an hour!"

In shop window:
EARS PIERCED WHILE YOU WAIT

In a department store:
BARGAIN BASEMENT UPSTAIRS

Lady in baker's shop: "I found a fly in one of your raisin buns yesterday!"

Shop assistant: "Well, bring it back and I'll exchange it for a raisin."

My mum went in the baker's. She said, "Got any bread left?"

He said, "Yes, ma'am."

She said, "You shouldn't have baked so much then."

Cuthbert Clutterbuck, not known for his great intelligence, returned to the car park after shopping just in time to see his car pull away and roar off at great speed. Dropping his packages, he fumbled in his pocket and produced a pen, and wrote hurriedly on the side of a parcel. Then he dashed off to find a policeman to report the theft.

"My car's just been stolen!" he cried, when he'd found an officer.

"Really," said the policeman. "What hard luck."

"But it's all right," said Cuthbert, producing the parcel. "I've got the swine's licence plate number right here!"

Customer: "I would like some bits for my dog, please."
Butcher: "Certainly, madam. What bits are missing?"

Sign in stationery window:
> *Calenders and Diaries*
> *All with 1 Year's Guarantee*

"Do you sell cat's meat?"
"Only if they're accompanied by a human being."

Two housewives were looking in the window of a fish-shop.
"That salmon looks nice, doesn't it, Gertie?" said one.
"That's not salmon, Elsie," said the other. "That's herring becoming red at the price they're asking for it!"

Read in the papers
Cathy Jones walked into a grocer's naked from the waist up, after the shop in Mid Glamorgan had put a sign in the window offering free groceries for the first topless lady customer who came in. Cathy had a long list of things to get for a party – since her third birthday was coming up shortly.

Law and disorder

The professor's wife decided to breed chickens as a hobby, but she did not have much luck. Finally someone told her that the Ministry of Agriculture distribute free information about poultry farming, so she wrote this letter:
"Dear Sir,
Every morning I find one or two of my prize chickens lying stiff and cold on the ground with their legs in the air. Would you be kind enough to tell me what is the matter?"
A few days later she got this reply:
"Dear Madam,
Your chickens are dead."

On an electricity pylon:
Danger! Touching these wires will result in instant death. Anyone found doing so will be prosecuted.

Claude: "When I grow up I want to be in the army."
Mother: "Why? You're only four now and I'm sure you'll change your mind as you get older."
Claude: "I won't change my mind. I want to be a soldier."
Mother: "But what if you get in a war and have to fight and get killed?"
Claude: "But who would want to kill me?"
Mother: "The enemy."
Claude: "That's all right then. I'll be in the enemy army."

There was a new clerk at the Poste Restante window in the post office. One day when he was busy, a man came to the window and asked, "Any letters for Mike Howe?"

The clerk went on working. The man repeated the question even louder.

Without looking up, the clerk answered, "Not for your cow, or your horse either."

NEWSFLASH!!

Thieves escaped with over half a million pounds from a Galway bank last night.

Police are trying to figure out the motive for the crime.

At the edge of a lake:

Any person passing beyond this notice will be drowned.

By order of the magistrates.

Excitable lady: "Hello! Police station? Help – come to my house quickly!"

Policeman: "What seems to be the trouble, madam?"

Excitable lady: "That dreadful new postman is sitting up in a tree in my front garden, teasing my dog."

A sweet old lady rang up the operator soon after a new telephone was put in her house.

"My telephone cord is too long," she said. "I wonder if you can help me out. Just pull it back a little from your end, will you?"

The sergeant had just finished his two-hour lecture on a soldier's duty and, looking at the sea of different faces, he wondered if his message had penetrated at all and whether it would be remembered. So, turning to one of them he asked:

"Now then, Private O'Grady, why should a soldier be ready to die for his country?"

The Irishman scratched his head for a while, then an enlightened smile moved across his face.

"Sure, sir," he said pleasantly, "you're quite right. Why should he?"

At a railway station:

Toilets out of order. Please use platforms 5 and 6.

A school inspector travelling in Limerick asked a young boy in class: "Who knocked down the Walls of Jericho?"

"It wasn't me, sir," said the boy nervously.

Furious with the low standard in the class, the inspector reported the story to the headmaster of the school.

"I asked a young lad, who knocked down the Walls of Jericho, and he told me that it wasn't him."

"The little rascal," said the headmaster, "I bet it was him all the time."

Even more furious, the inspector went to the school governor and repeated the story.

"Well," said the school governor, "the boy comes of an honest family, and you can take it from me, that if he says he didn't knock down the Walls of Jericho, then he is telling the truth."

Finally, in despair, the inspector reported the whole affair to the Department of Education.

He received the following communication:
"Dear Sir,
With regard to your recent letter concerning the Walls of Jericho, we would like to inform you that this matter does not fall within the jurisdiction of this department. We therefore suggest that you refer the problem to the Building Department."

Did you hear about the policeman who gave out a hundred parking tickets before he realized he was in a drive-in movie?

The police patrol-car driver was shocked to see, as he overtook a fast-moving car, that the woman at the wheel was knitting. He wound down his window and shouted, "Pull over!"
"No," she called back. "A pair of socks!"

Seeing a woman standing helplessly by her car in a remote part of the countryside, the kindly policeman got off his bicycle and asked what was the matter. "Oh, thank you, officer," she said. "I've had a flat tyre. I've managed to change the wheel, but now I can't lower the jack."
"Very good, madam," said the policeman. "I'll see what I can do."
"But please lower the car gently," said the woman. "My husband's asleep in the back seat!"

Read in the papers

After the city council at Guayaquil, Ecuador, had decided to erect a statue to the Ecuadorian poet Jose Olmedo, they found there was not enough money to pay for an original work.

It was then decided to buy a second-hand statue of the English poet Lord Byron, and change the name.

Fighting in the thick of the Falklands War, Scots Guardsman Alex Blair was pleased to hear there was a letter from home for him.

It proved to be from Strathclyde Regional Council threatening him with legal action over an unpaid parking fine.

In 1974 the Bramber Parish Council voted to save electricity by going without street lighting for three days. After the experiment the parish treasurer announced that electricity to the value of £ 11.59 had been saved. The satisfied faces of the listeners soon changed, however, after hearing that switching off the electricity had cost £ 18.48 and switching it on again another £ 12. It had, therefore, cost the council £ 18.89 to spend three days in darkness.

The residents of Bennet Court, an Old Folks Home in Otley, Yorkshire, had long wanted a fence around their home to give it more privacy. Early in 1979 the Leeds Council workers arrived in their lorry with picks, shovels and planks of wood. They took five days to erect the 3½ feet high and 100 yards long fence. After they had completed it they noticed that they had not left a gap to drive their lorry out.

"It was like watching a Laurel and Hardy film," said Mrs Elizabeth Ann Whittaker. "You could see them looking at the fence, then at the lorry, then at the fence again. Some of us had wondered about the lorry, but we didn't want to interfere."

A council spokesman said: "It was an oversight. Maybe they got carried away in their work." The workers returned next morning to knock down part of the fence and get their lorry.

Acting on Government orders, Northamptonshire County Council built an underground fall-out shelter for officials who would control emergency services following a nuclear attack.

They could live there safely for weeks, unless they need to use the loo. It is outside.

Police raced to the scene when a passer-by reported that he had found a safe standing beside the road. One man stood guard, detectives took fingerprints, then a Land Rover arrived to carry it back to the station at Halesowen, West Midlands. But they couldn't shift it – because it was an electricity board junction box, firmly cemented into the ground.

Tired of letters he posted going astray, John Forster, Cambridge wrote on the back of one: 'To any employees of the GPO who may have a hand in sorting this letter, kindly note that it is addressed to *Scarborough,* in the North Riding of Yorkshire, and *not* to Knaresborough, Guisborough, Bradford, Catterick army camp or Cleckheaton, to several of which places you have on previous occasions delivered my clearly addressed letters.'

The letter was delivered to Great Yarmouth.

A Canadian murder trial had to be abandoned in 1978 when it was discovered that one juror spoke no English, another was deaf, and a third suffered from both these problems.

A man parachuted onto a four-lane highway near Joliet, Illinois, USA, and was accused by police of not using an authorized entrance.

After much research into poisons and traps, efficiency and cost-effectiveness, a team at Ohio State University determined, for the benefit of farmers, the best method of keeping down mice and rats. It's called a cat.

Animal antics

If you saw 9 elephants outside Woolworth's with blue socks and one elephant outside Harrod's with red socks, what would that prove?
That 9 out of 10 elephants wear blue socks.

Read in the papers
If you're thinking of changing the colour of your hair, be careful where you take a nap. A German punk-rock fan who had dyed his hair green fell asleep in a pedestrian precinct in Bielefeld. He woke up when a camel advertising a local circus started nibbling at his head. We can only hope he was called Herr Gras!

Why did Noah name the big animal an elephant?
Because it looked more like an elephant than any other animal.

Teacher: "Name a bird that doesn't build its own nest."
Student: "The cuckoo."
Teacher: "Very good. How do you know?"
Student: "Simple – everyone knows the cuckoo lives in a clock!"

Define willpower.
"An elephant eating only one peanut."

I hear that at the local zoo they are trying to cross a carrier pigeon with a woodpecker: they are aiming to breed a bird that will not only deliver messages but also knock first.

Why did the sparrow fly into the library?
It was looking for bookworms.

Lucy: "Is it correct to say that you water your horse?"
Mother: "Yes, dear."
Lucy: "Then I'm going to milk the cat."

What do you get if you cross an octopus with a cow?
An animal that can milk itself.

What does an elephant do if it breaks a toe?
Gives up ballet dancing.

I rode a well-mannered horse – whenever we came to jump over a fence it let me go first!

Two big tortoises and a little one came into a café and ordered three banana splits. While they were waiting to be served they noticed it had started to rain.
"We ought to have our umbrella," said one of the big tor-

toises, and the other big one agreed. They decided that the little tortoise should go home and get the umbrella. He did not want to go because he was afraid the two big tortoises would eat his banana split. But they promised not to, and finally the little tortoise started off.

A week passed, then two weeks. At the end of the third week one of the big tortoises said, "Oh, come on, let's eat his banana split."

"Okay, let's," said the other.

"If you do, I won't go for that umbrella," screamed the little tortoise, sticking his head out from under the counter at the other end of the café.

Ivan: "You can tell the age of a horse by the teeth."
Andrea: "But who wants to bite a horse?"

Joel: "Why is it that every time the doorbell rings your dog goes into his corner?"
Richard: "It's because he's a boxer."

Noah: "I thought we had two turkeys when we set sail?"
Mrs Noah: "Well, dear, it *is* Christmas..."

What's brown, has three humps, and lives in the desert?
A camel with a rucksack.

Why do elephants paint their feet yellow?
So they can hide upside down in custard.

When do elephants paint their toe-nails red?
When they want to hide in strawberry jam.

What do geese eat?
Gooseberries.

What's brown, has two humps, and is found at the South Pole?
A lost camel.

Why don't you ever see chickens in the zoo?
Because they can't afford the admission.

Baby Sardine: "Mummy, what's a submarine?"
Mother Sardine: "It's just a tin of people, darling."

What goes black and white, black and white, black and white, black and white?
A penguin rolling down a hill.

Read in the papers
London Zoo won a contract to supply a zoo in the Middle East desert state of Qatar with six camels.

What's black and white and makes a dreadful noise?
A penguin playing the bagpipes.

A gorilla was walking through the jungle when he came across a deer eating grass in a clearing. The gorilla roared, "Who is the king of the jungle?" and the deer replied, "Oh, you are, Master."

The gorilla walked off pleased. Soon he came across a zebra drinking at a water hole. The gorilla roared, "Who is the king of the jungle?" and the zebra replied, "Oh, you are, Master."

The gorilla walked off pleased. Then he came across an elephant. "Who is the king of the jungle?" he roared. With that, the elephant threw the gorilla across a tree and jumped on him. The gorilla scraped himself off the ground and said, "Okay, okay, there's no need to get mad just because you don't know the answer."

The wealthy man booked the royal box at the London theatre so that he could take his pet elephant with him to watch the play.

Everyone was surprised at how well the elephant behaved and the manager of the theatre commented on this: "Your elephant certainly seemed to enjoy himself. I could see him paying close attention to everything. I must say I was somewhat surprised that he should like the play so much."

"So was I," replied the wealthy man. "When he read the book the play was based on he didn't like it at all."

What animal in Noah's Ark didn't come in pairs?
Worms, they came in apples.

What should you do if you find a gorilla in your bed?
Sleep somewhere else.

Two cats were looking at a bird in a cage.
"That's not a canary," said the first cat. "It's green."
"You never know," said the second. "Maybe it's not ripe yet."

I don't know who lives there, but they get an awful lot of letters!

Bill: "What kind of dog is that?"
Will: "He's a police dog."
Bill: "He doesn't look like one to me."
Will: "Of course not. He's in the secret service."

Louise: "I went riding this morning."
Anne: "Horseback?"
Louise: "Yes, we came back together."

A friend of mine has just invented a wonderful new insecticide. You spray it on all your plants and it promptly kills them so that the insects will then starve to death.

Little Sandra stared a long time at the stork in the zoo, then turned at last to her mother and sighed, "He never even recognized me!"

Gorilla: "Doctor, my hair keeps falling out. What can you give me to keep it in?"
Doctor: "Try this cardboard box."

Teacher: "What family does the rhinoceros belong to?"
Pupil: "I don't know, Miss - nobody in our street has one."

"Have you ever seen a man-eating tiger?"
"No, but I once saw a man eating chicken."

A woodpecker was talking to a chicken. "Woodpeckers are much cleverer than you chickens."
"What makes you say that?" asked the chicken. "You seem to spend all your day banging your head against a tree."
"Ah!" responded the woodpecker. "But have you ever heard of Kentucky Fried Woodpecker?"

Back to nature

"What a strange-looking cow," said the young girl from the big city. "Why doesn't it have horns?"
"Well," answered the farmer, "some cows are born without horns, some shed their horns, some are dehorned, while some breeds don't have horns at all. So you see, there are lots of reasons why cows might not have horns but the reason why that particular animal hasn't got horns is because it isn't a cow – it's a horse!"

Hopeful boy: "Good river for fish?"
Fisherman: "It must be. I can't get any of them to come out."

"You're all very lucky to be living in such a beautiful part of the country," said a visiting bishop to Alec's class. "The land is truly flowing with milk and honey. I don't suppose any of you know where that comes from, do you?"
"We're not that stupid," said Alec. "Milk comes from cows and honey from bees."

Dinny and Dave, farmers, met one day at a Kilkenny fair.
"Tell me," said Dinny, "what did you give your mule when he had colic?"
"Turpentine," said Dave.
A few months later they met again.

"What did you say you gave your mule when he had colic?" said Dave.

"Well, I gave my mule turpentine, and he died," said Dinny.

"So did mine," said Dave, "so did mine."

Two goats were roaming the pasture when they found an old discarded reel of film. As they proceeded to eat the celluloid, one goat said, "Good, don't you think?"

"Oh, I don't know," replied the other goat, "I think the book was much better."

Look at a cow and remember that the greatest scientists have never discovered how to turn grass into milk!

Jones: "Why were all your chickens out in the front garden yesterday?"

Brown: "They heard that men were coming here to lay a pavement, and they wanted to see how it was done."

Patrick's pregnant wife lived way out in the country and took ill one day shortly before her child was due. It was quite dark when the doctor arrived and he asked, "Where is the little lady, Patrick?"

"She's over there in the stable where she collapsed."

With Patrick holding the lamp the doctor set about his job.

"Patrick, you're the proud father of a little boy."

Patrick said, "Doctor, we'll have a drink."

"Just a minute. Hold the light a little closer. You're the father of two."

"We'll open a bottle," said Patrick.

"Wait," the doctor said. "Hold the light a little closer. You're the father of three."

"And sure it's going to be a celebration and all," said Patrick.

"Just a minute," said the doctor. "Hold the light a little closer."

"I don't want to be difficult, doctor," said Patrick, "but do you think this bloody light's attracting them?"

"I met a farmer who's a magician."

"How do you know?"

"He told me he was going to turn his cow into a field."

In a country lane:
When this sign is under water the road is closed to traffic.

Instructor at riding academy: "What kind of saddle do you want – one with a horn, or one without?"

Dude: "Without, I think. There doesn't seem to be much traffic round here."

A tourist went into a field on Farmer Giles' land and began to pick flowers. Suddenly he noticed a bull in the field, and called out: "Is that bull safe?"

"Offhand," Farmer Giles answered, "I'd say he's a lot safer than you are."

Timothy O'Leary bought Sean Casey's horse for £ 100 cash. Sean got to thinking that since Tim paid the price so willingly, the horse must be worth more. Next day he bought the horse back for £ 200. Later Tim again bought the horse – for £ 300. This kept going on until the price went up to £ 1.500.

Then a Limerick horse trader came on the scene and bought the horse from Sean for £ 2.000.

Hearing of this, Tim hurried over to Sean and said angrily: "You are a fool, selling that mare. Both of us were making a good living off her!"

The lorry driver was in Eastleigh in Hampshire when he slowed down his lorry and then stopped. Winding down the window of his cab he called out to a middle-aged lady: "Excuse me, madam, but can you tell me the way to Southampton?"

"I'm sorry, I don't know," replied the lady.

"Well, do you know which direction Winchester is in?"

"No."

"Huh!" muttered the lorry driver. "They can't be far from here and yet you don't know which direction they're in. You don't appear to know much."

"At least," responded the lady, "I am not the one who is lost!"

"I can't decide whether to buy a bicycle or a cow for my farm."

"Won't you look silly riding a cow?"

"I'd look even sillier trying to milk a bicycle."

A tourist in Cornwall was filling up his petrol tank late at night when he noticed a smile on the garage attendant's face.

"I say, what's the big joke?" the tourist asked.

"Well, you're the last person to be served at the old price."

The tourist had the pleasant feeling of finding a bargain.

"Really?", he smiled. "Why is that?"

"Well," the attendant replied, "from tomorrow, the price goes down twenty pence a gallon!"

Read in the papers

1912 saw the most spectacular Oxford and Cambridge boat race ever – in which both crews sank. It was shortly after Oxford had taken an early lead that the fiasco began. As water began to come into their boat the crew decided to make for the river bank where they all jumped out, upturned the boat and jumped in again. All except one of the oarsmen, who disappeared into the crowd. The rest of the crew could hardly believe their ears when he returned, explaining that he had spotted an old friend named Boswell and had gone to have a chat with him. The cox asked him politely if he wouldn't mind getting back into the boat, as they were in the middle of a race. The oarsman obliged, saying 'goodbye' to Boswell and the race continued.

No sooner were they on the water again than they saw the Cambridge crew go past. They were, however, swimming, as their boat was underwater.

By this time the Thames was full of boats and oarsmen. Rescue boats appeared and the most chaotic race ever was abandoned.

If country air is so good –
Why don't they build cities in the country?

Sam: "What a lovely colour that cow is!"
Farmer: "It's a Jersey."
Sam: "Really? I thought it was her skin."

Motorist: "Could you tell me how to get to Grantham from here?"
Countryman: "Well, go back along this road for a few miles and then take the first turning on the left. No, wait, maybe it's the second turning on the left. Come to think of it, if I was trying to get to Grantham, I wouldn't start from here at all."

There was once a terrible golfer who hit a ball on to an ant hill. He walked up to the ant hill and tried to hit the ball, but no matter how many swings he took, he only ever hit the ant hill, killing the ants. Eventually there were only two ants left. One looked at the other and said, "If we want to stay alive, I suppose, we'd better get on that ball."

An old farmer was showing a group of city children around the countryside one day.

"Well, look here," he said. "I've found a horseshoe. Anyone know what that means?"

"Yeah," said the show-off, "one of your horses is walking around in his socks."

Three men were sitting on a park bench. The two on the outside were acting as if they were fishing – casting out their lines, holding their rods ... The man in the middle was reading a newspaper.

A policeman walked by and stopped when he saw what the two men were doing. He was a little surprised and asked the man in the middle if he knew the two men sitting on either side of him.

"Oh, yes," said the man, "they're my friends."

"Well, get them out of here," said the policeman.

"Yes, sir!" said the man, and he began to row wildly.

"Tell me," said the hiker to a local, "will this pathway take me to the main road?"

"No, sir," replied the rustic, "you'll have to go by yourself."

An extremely rich businessman found himself in a small Lancashire hotel where his wealth and importance seemed to be quite unknown, and to his annoyance he was treated with no more and no less respect than any other guest. Determined to show his worth, at breakfast he said loudly to the waiter, "Bring me £ 10 worth of bacon and eggs!" Not the least ashamed, the waiter said, "Sorry, sir, but we don't serve half-portions!"

It was local election time in the countryside and the candidate was calling round all the houses in his area. At one house the door was answered by a small boy. "Tell me, young man," said the politician, "is your Mummy in the Labour Party or the Conservative Party?"
"Neither," said the boy, "she's in the toilet."

A huge American car screeched to a halt in a sleepy Warwickshire village, and the driver called out to a local inhabitant, "Say – am I on the right road for Shakespeare's birthplace?"
"Ar, straight on, sir," said the rustic, "but no need to hurry. He's dead."

Two boys went fishing one summer's morning and trespassed on to the Squire's land. The gamekeeper spotted them and came running up.
"Didn't you see the notice?" he roared.
"Yes," said the more quick-witted boy of the two, "but it said 'Private' at the top so we didn't like to read any further."

Little Susie was staying with her grandmother in the country for a few days.
"Would you like to see the cuckoo come out of the cuckoo clock?" asked her grandmother.
"I'd rather see Grandpa come out of the grandfather clock," said Susie.

Specialist treatment

Receptionist: "The doctor will be able to see you on May 7th."
Patient: "No sooner than that? I could be dead by then."
Receptionist: "Never mind, you can always cancel your appointment."

Patient: "Doctor, if this swelling in my leg gets any worse I won't be able to get my trousers on."
Doctor: "Don't worry, I'll give you a prescription."
Patient: "What's it for?"
Doctor: "A kilt."

Mrs Casey accompanied her daughter Kathleen to her appointment with Dr Flynn and explained the situation.
"Sure, she's been having some strange symptoms and I'm worried about her."
Dr Flynn examined Kathleen carefully and then announced, "Sure, it's pregnant your daughter is."
"Saints preserve us! Will you be listening to that. My daughter pregnant! I've never heard such nonsense, indeed I haven't" and she turned to Kathleen for confirmation.
Kathleen's face became red and she replied, "No, no, of course not. I've never even kissed a man!"
Flynn looked from mother to daughter and back again.

Then, silently he stood up and walked to the window. He stared out and continued to stare with great concentration.

Finally Mrs Casey could stand it no longer and asked, "Doctor, is there something wrong out there?"

"No," said Flynn. "Sure, it's just that the last time anything like this happened, a star appeared in the East and I was looking to see if another one was going to show up at all. Three fellows showed up with gifts of gold and other precious things and I don't want to miss them this time."

Doctor: "What seems to be your trouble?"

Patient: "After I get up in the morning, I'm always dizzy for half an hour."

Doctor: "Then why don't you get up half an hour later?"

Three young medical students were discussing the theory of pre-natal influence.

"It's obviously an absurd theory," one said. "It's been disproved every time it's investigated. For example, before I was born, my mother broke a huge pile of LP records. But it's never bothered me ... bothered me ... bothered me."

Read in the papers

A Norfolk woman complained to her doctor about a pain in her mouth – and had a tomato plant removed from beneath her false teeth.

A wide-eyed character who was convinced he was Napoleon burst into a psychiatrist's office, pushed his hand inside his coat, and declared, "It isn't myself I've come to see you about, doctor. It's my wife, Josephine. She thinks she's Mrs Richardson."

"Doctor, can you give me something for my liver?"
"How about a pound of onions."

The doctor stood by the bedside, and looked down at the sick man.
"I cannot hide from you the fact that you are very ill," he said. "Is there anyone you would like to see?"
"Yes," replied the patient faintly. "Another doctor."

Doctor: "Now, tell me, have you ever had any trouble with diarrhoea?"
Patient: "Only once."
Doctor: "And when was that?"
Patient: "When I was at school and was asked to spell it."

Surgeon to colleague: "We operated just in time. A couple more days and he would have recovered without us."

Patient: "Can this operation be performed successfully, doctor?"
Doctor: "That's what we're about to find out ..."

"I'm afraid I've adopted a terrible habit," the patient told his psychiatrist. "Wherever I am, I can't help talking to myself. Is there anything you can do for me?"
"I suppose there is," the psychiatrist replied. "But I should warn you it will be a long, slow, painful treatment, and very expensive as well. But suppose you do talk to yourself. Is that so bad?"
"No, I guess it isn't," the patient agreed. "But I'm so boring."

"Doctor, can you give me something for my hands – they shake all the time."
"Do you drink a lot?"
"No, doctor, I spill most of it".

An inscription on the tombstone of a hypochondriac reads:

I TOLD YOU I WAS ILL

John saw a small crowd by the roadside, and pulled up in his car to see what it was all about.
He saw a man on the ground, having an epileptic fit.
As he approached the man, an elderly lady pushed him

away, saying: "Leave him alone. I have given him all the first aid." The elderly woman then ran into her house, and came out a few minutes later with a First Aid Hand Book.

She knelt down beside the man having epileptic fit, and started to turn over the pages.

John tried to feel the man's pulse, but the lady brushed him aside.

"I'm sorry to disturb you", he said finally. "Carry on the good work according to the book, and when you come to the part about sending for the doctor ... That's ME!"

Two psychiatrists bumped into each other in the Consultant's lounge.

"How am I feeling?" said the first.

"Fine, fine, you're feeling fine. How am I feeling?" replied the second.

Read in the papers
One foggy morning two German motorists were rushed to hospital suffering from head injuries after the most unusual head-on collision. With visibility down to a matter of feet, both drivers had been moving down the carriageway at a snail's pace, with their heads stuck out of their windows to follow the lines in the centre of the road, when they met face to face.

Patient: "Tell me honestly, doctor, what's the matter with me?"
Doctor: "You eat too much, drink too much, and you're the laziest man I've ever treated."
Patient: "Terrific, but do you think you could pop that into Latin, so that I can take a week off work?"

Doctor: "Did those pills I gave you help you sleep any better?"
Patient: "Well, I slept – but still dreamed that I didn't."

Amelia didn't know what to do with her seven-year-old son, Reginald. Every time a visitor came to the house or he saw someone he didn't know he would race towards them and bite them on the knee. Then he would cling to their legs and refuse to let go.
Eventually, Amelia took Reginald to a child psychologist and, on seeing the psychologist Reginald rushed towards him, bit his knee and then clung to the man's legs.
The child psychologist looked down at Reginald, then bent and whispered something in the boy's ear. Immedi-

ately, Reginald let go of the man's legs and ran back to his mother.

"He's cured!" cried Amelia. "What did you say to him?"

The child psychologist smiled and said: "I told him that if he didn't let go of my legs I'd smash his stupid face in."

"We like you so much better than the last doctor," one patient of a home for mentally ill people told a new member of staff.

"That's very kind of you," answered the doctor. "Why?"

"You seem more like one of us," said the patient.

"The patient here limps because one leg is shorter than the other," remarked the professor to a group of medical students. Turning to one of them, he asked, "What would you do in a case like this?"

The student thought for a moment before replying, "I think that under those circumstances, I would probably limp too."

"Doctor, last year you told me to avoid dampness if I wanted my rheumatism to get better."

"That's right – has it helped?"

"Yes. But can I have a bath this year?"

"Doctor, I feel terrible," the conservative business executive complained. "What's wrong with me?"

"Well, just answer a few questions first," the doctor said. "Do you drink much alcohol?"

"I never touch a drop."

"Do you smoke?" the doctor continued.

"No, tobacco's a filthy weed," the businessman replied.

"Do you spend many late nights?"

"Of course not!" the patient retorted. "I'm in bed every night by ten-thirty – early to bed and early to rise, that's my motto."

"Well, then, are you experiencing sharp pains in the head?"

"Yes, yes, I suffer from them all the time."

"Just what I thought," the doctor smiled. "Your halo is on too tight!"

The Health Minister, visiting a mental hospital had difficulty getting the telephone connection to London.

Furiously he shouted to the operator, "Young lady, do you know who I am?"

"No", was the calm reply, "but I know where you are."

Read in the papers
An elderly Sydney man who, in spite of wearing a hearing-aid for twenty-five years, had become increasingly harder of hearing, visited his local hospital to see if anything could be done to help him. In the course of the examination, the doctor removed the hearing-aid and when replacing it, accidentally popped it in the other ear. The moment he did this, perfect clarity returned, and the patient heard properly for the first time in a quarter of a century – ever since the ear-piece was originally fitted in the wrong ear.

A trade union leader went to his doctor for help in getting to sleep. The doctor did not want to put the union leader on sleeping pills until other remedies had been tried and so he asked the man to lie quite still in bed at night and count sheep.

The trade union leader did this, but by the time he'd counted the twenty-seventh sheep they'd all gone on strike for shorter hours and lower fences.

An Indian opened the door to a doctor's waiting-room and walked straight through to the door of the surgery on the other side, ignoring the other patients dutifully waiting to be called in. As he was about to open the door, a woman jumped up, caught him by the arm and said in a loud, distinct voice: "No. We before you. You take your turn. Understand?"

The Indian answered in the same careful tones: "No. You after me. Me doctor. Understand?"

"You can have that brain there for £ 3.000," said the brain surgeon to the man who was going to have a brain transplant. "It used to belong to a bank manager. This one's £ 5.000: it was a dancer's. And this one's £ 50.000: it belonged to a school teacher."

"Why's it ten times more than the others?" the man wanted to know.

"It's been used ten times less than theirs!"

Doctor: "Have you had this before?"
Man: "Yes."
Doctor: "Well, I'm sorry to say you've got it again."

Read in the papers
A sixteenth-century Jewish doctor is credited with having performed one of the earliest blood transfusions on Pope Innocent VIII., who was ill. Selecting three healthy boys as donors, the doctor set about his work. Of the five participants, however, only one survived this medical breakthrough – and that was the doctor.

Love makes the world go round

It was a wet stormy day when Mike buried his wife Kathleen. Just as the funeral party left the graveyard there was a bright flash of lightning and a loud rumble of thunder.

Pat looked up at the sky and commented: "She's arrived up there already."

Read in the papers
Jerry and Kathryn Sluckin had a very short married life. One hour after the wedding ceremony at Kensington registry office in November 1975 Kathryn announced to her surprised husband and relatives, "It won't work". She left the wedding party. Her husband later heard that his wife was living in a meditation commune in Finchley.

"I had a few doubts before the wedding," she admitted afterwards, "but didn't want to say anything."

Maurice forgot to tell his wife Florrie that he'd painted the toilet seat, with the inevitable result – Florrie and the throne became as one, inseparable.

Maurice, acting swiftly before panic could set in, took off the seat from the pedestal and, tucking his wife's dress neatly over the problem, took his wife to the local doctor. There he rushed her past waiting patients and into the consulting room, where he bared her all for the doctor's inspection.

"Yes, very attractive," the bemused doctor admitted. "But why did you have it framed?"

Who's Santa Claus's wife?
Mary Christmas.

"I hear your first three husbands died of mushroom poisoning, and now you claim your fourth died falling over a cliff. Isn't that a bit odd?"
"Not really. He didn't like mushrooms."

"In some countries," said the geography teacher, "men are allowed more than one wife. That's called polygamy. In others, women are allowed more than one husband. That's called polyandry. In this country, men and women are allowed only one married partner. Can anyone tell me what that's called?"
"Monotony, sir?"

Mr and Mrs Jones were writing thank-you letters for presents they had received on their silver wedding anniversary. Suddenly Mr Jones stopped. He looked worried.
"What's the matter, dear?" asked Mrs Jones.
"I had it on the tip of my tongue, and now it's gone," replied Mr Jones.
"Just think hard and it will come back to you," Mrs Jones said.
"Thinking won't bring it back. It was a 19 p stamp," said Mr Jones.

The absent-minded professor came home and told his wife he felt ill because he had been travelling backwards for two hours on the train.

"Why didn't you ask the person opposite you to change seats with you?" his wife asked.

"I couldn't," the absent-minded professor said. "There wasn't anybody sitting opposite me."

My husband wears clothes that will never go out of style – they'll always look ridiculous.

Mr Bloggs: "You've got to help me. My wife is absolutely unbearable. She insists on keeping a pet pig in the bedroom and the smell is terrible."
Marriage guidance counsellor: "Why don't you open the bedroom window and let the smell out?"
Mr Bloggs:"What? And let all my geese and pigeons escape?"

If the bride wears white for her wedding as a symbol of purity and joy – then why does the groom always wear the opposite, black?

Read in the papers
Because his fiancee had recovered from a serious illness, Paul Bonfirm walked halfway across Brazil carrying a wooden cross.
In his absence she married another man.

Woman: "My husband has left me and he took the dog."
Neighbour: "Oh no – not that beautiful dog!"

"I was told you buried your husband last week."
"Had to. Dead, you know."

George: "Sir, I don't quite know how to ask this."
Mr Smith: "Ask what?"
George: "Well, I'd like your daughter for my wife."
Mr Smith: "Don't be ridiculous! I know we live in liberated times, but I don't think I'd like my daughter to go off with your wife."

I thought the television programmes had improved tremendously – until my wife told me I'd been watching the fish tank she'd swopped for the TV.

One morning Pat received a letter in the post warning him: "If you don't send £ 5.000 to the above address immediately, we will kidnap your wife Bridget and you will never see her again."

Pat sent the following reply:

"Dear Sir,

I haven't got £ 5.000, but your offer interests me greatly."

Simon and Sarah were snuggled up on the sofa when Simon said: "You know, I've been thinking. For the past few years I've been content just living on my own. But now I feel the need for a faithful companion. Someone who will always be there when I come home. Someone who will look at me with devotion in their eyes. Someone who ..."

Sarah interrupted him: "That's a great idea! Shall we go to the pet shop together and I'll help you choose the puppy?"

Read in the papers

Marjorie Mumblebelly, from Sydney, Australia, longed for the day when she could change her name. When she married, she became Mrs Jerry Cosybottom.

Another Australian girl had the same problem. Her maiden name was Janet Sewer. She married William Smellie.

John: "Would you say that I am very vain?"
Sarah: "No, of course not. Why?"
John: "Well, other men as handsome, intelligent and sexy as me usually are very vain."

"Am I the only man you've ever kissed?"
"Indeed you are, but not the best-looking."

Ronald: "All my wife says to me is 'Money, money,' she's always asking for money."
Tom: "Why does she need so much? What does she spend it on?"
Ronald: "I've no idea. I never give her any."

A middle-aged couple arrived at the doctor's surgery, the wife helping her husband through the door and into a chair. When they were called, the man got to his feet in obvious pain, and bent at the waist, shuffled into the doctor's consulting room.

"Arthritis with complications?" asked the receptionist sympathetically.

"Do-it-yourself," replied the wife sarcastically, "with concrete paving slabs."

Don't let this spoil
your appetite

Barmaid: "I'm sorry, sir, the bar will not be open for half an hour – would you like a drink while you're waiting?"

There are four kinds of milk – sweet milk, sour milk, buttermilk and condensed milk. This explains why dairy cows are equipped with four taps!

The old man had never been in an expensive restaurant and it was one of the things he longed to do before he died, so he carefully saved a little of his pension money each week and eventually he had enough money to dine out in style.
Unfortunately, he had a rude shock when he tied his table napkin around his neck and the head waiter in the restaurant said to him: "Would sir like a shave or a haircut?"

Read in the papers
A set of false teeth was found in a cake dropped behind a tree at a Buckingham Palace garden party.

Dinner lady: "Alec! Eat your greens. They're good for growing children."
Alec: "Who wants to grow children?"

Boy (eating an apple): "Gosh! I just swallowed a worm."

Neighbour: "Come into the house and I'll give you something for it."

Boy: "No, thanks, I'll just let it starve."

"It says on the menu that there's a choice of greens," said Alec to the dinner lady.

"There is," said she. "Broccoli."

"But that's no choice."

"Yes it is," said the dinner lady. "Take it or leave it."

"I went to a restaurant where there were no menus."

"How did you know what there was to eat?"

"I just looked at the tablecloth and guessed."

"Are you a good boy, Charles?" asked the visitor. "Do you say your prayers before each meal?"
"Oh no," said Charles, "my mum's cooking has improved a lot."

How can you improve the taste of salt?
Sprinkle it lightly over chips.

Granny: "You've left all your crusts, Joan. When I was your age I ate every one."
Joan: "Do you still like crusts, Grandma?"
Granny: "Yes I do."
Joan: "Well, you can have mine."

"Waiter, waiter, I have a complaint."
"This is a restaurant, sir, not a hospital."

There were two eggs in a saucepan. One egg said, "Whoo, it's hot in here." The other one said, "Wait till you get out, you'll get your head bashed in."

Read in the papers
When a woman complained that a piece of steak she had bought tasted like cardboard, Hertfordshire trading standards officers found that was just what it was.
She had grilled a sheet of cardboard put in the package.

A woman woke her husband up and said,
"there's a burglar in the kitchen eating the cake I made this afternoon. Ring 999!"
"Who shall I ask for?" said her husband, "police or ambulance?"

A man went into a milk bar and ordered a milk shake. He drank it to the last drop, smacking his lips every now and then. At last he said to the man behind the counter, "That was the best milk shake I ever had. Just to show you how much I enjoyed it, I want you to take this for a present."
He reached into his pocket and pulled out a live lobster.
The man did not know exactly what to do, but finally he said, "Thanks very much. I'll take it home for dinner."
"Oh, she's already had dinner," said the customer. "Take her to the pictures."

In an office kitchen:
Staff should empty teapots and then stand upside down on the draining board.

What's worse than finding a maggot in your apple?
Finding half a maggot.

How do you make a sausage roll?
Push it.

What does a traffic warden have in his sandwiches?
Traffic jam.

A man came into a café and ordered a strawberry parfait in a long, tall glass. When it came, he carefully spooned off the whipped cream and rubbed it in his hair. Then he tossed the ice-cream behind the counter and eagerly ate up the glass. Finally he threw the stem of the glass over his shoulder.

Another customer, who had been watching the performance, tapped his arm. "My good man," he said, "what are you thinking of?"

"I'll tell you," was the answer. "Whipped cream is good for the hair. I can't stand ice-cream. It's too cold. But I just love glass."

"Of course, of course! But my good man," said the other, "don't you realize that the stem is the best part?"

Mum: "Don't you know you're not supposed to eat with your knife?"
Child: "Yes, but my fork leaks."

What do scientists eat?
Microchips.

"Now then Godfrey," Mrs Hamilton asked in a friendly way, "will you join us in a cup of tea?"
"No thank you," replied Godfrey, "there's hardly room for you let alone two of us."

Vegetarian: "I've lived on nothing but vegetables for years."
Listener: "So what, I've lived on Earth all my life."

HOW DO YOU **KNOW** YOU DON'T LIKE IT? YOU'VE NEVER **HAD** FRIED EGG AND CUSTARD BEFORE!

"John, have you finished your alphabet soup?"
"Not yet, I'm only up to the Ms."

Jeffrey: "We have a Red Indian toaster at home."
Jeremy: "What's a Red Indian toaster?"
Jeffrey: "Instead of the toast popping up it sends up smoke signals."

"Eat your dinner."
"I'm waiting for the mustard to cool."

What vegetable should you pick to go with jacket potatoes?
Button mushrooms.

Read in the papers

Iran is not exactly a Mecca for beer lovers. True, you can easily find non-alcoholic varieties, but that's a bit like buying sugar-free honey or champagne without bubbles.

Iranians with a flair for brew-it-yourself have got around the problem by adding a bit of yeast and a package or two of sugar to store-bought beer. When it comes to testing the finished product they are fairly inventive too. They hold a lighted match above the brew. If it blows out, or if the beer explodes, it's not yet ready to be bottled. Or drunk.

First Girl: "Here, try one of these cakes I've just made."
Second Girl: "Ugh, it's horrible!"
First Girl: "You've no taste. It definitely says in my cookery book that these cakes are delicious."

"Waiter, waiter, there's a fly in my soup!"
"If you throw it a pea it will play water polo."

"Waiter, I'll have an egg. No, make it a steak."
"I'm a waiter, sir, not a magician."

"Waiter, how long will my spaghetti be?"
"No idea, sir, we never measure it."

The waitress brought Mr Jones his soup, and then stood looking out of the window.

"It looks like rain," she said.

"Yes," replied Mr Jones having started his soup, "it tastes like rain as well."

Customer: "Waiter! Get me the chef!"

Waiter: "Certainly, sir."

Chef: "You wanted me, sir?"

Customer: "I most certainly did! This steak and kidney pie is as hard as old rocks. It's absolutely terrible!"

Chef: "But my steak and kidney pies are delicious. I've had lots of experience making them. Indeed, I've been making them since before you were born."

Customer: "So why did you have to wait until now to serve them?"

"Waiter, there's a fly in my butter."

"No there isn't."

"Yes there is."

"I tell you there isn't for two reasons: one, it's a moth, and two, it's not butter, it's margarine."

"Waiter, what kind of bird is this?"

"It's a wood pigeon."

"I thought so – bring me the saw."

"Waiter, there's a fly in my soup."

"Don't worry, sir, that spider on your bread will get him."

"Waiter, do I have to sit here until I die of starvation?"
"No sir, we close at seven."

Customer: "Do you serve lamb?"
Waiter: "I'm sorry, sir, we don't allow animals to dine here."

"Waiter, what's this fly doing in my alphabet soup?"
"I expect he's learning to read."

Read in the papers

A clever whisky-loving fisherman in Street, Somerset, put his hobby to ill gain one night when he stole a bottle of expensive whisky from an off-licence. He pushed his rod through the shop's letter box, hooked a bottle off the shelf and drew it towards the door with his fishing line. Manipulating the neck up through the letter box he poured the contents into his own bottle and got away.

"Waiter, I'd like a steak, please."
"Would you like anything with it?"
"If it's anything like the last one I had here you'd better bring me a hammer and chisel."

Absent-minded, crazy-minded, stupid-minded

Paddy and Mick were kept in a high security prison, but they developed an ingenious method of communicating with each other by means of a secret code and banging on the pipes.

However, their communication broke down when they were transferred to different cells.

How do you drown a hundred idiot sailors?
Get them to push-start a submarine.

Why do idiots usually walk around in groups of three?
Because one can read, one can write and the third feels proud to hang around with the smart kids in the area.

The absent-minded professor was in his study. The telephone rang, and his assistant said, "It's a long-distance from London."
"Quite right," said the professor and went on reading.

"Oh dear! Oh dear!" moaned the absent-minded professor. He was standing in a bus, holding on to the rail with one hand while with his other hand he clutched a number of parcels.
"Is there anything I can do to help you, sir?" asked a friendly fellow-passenger.

"Why, yes, there is, if you don't mind," said the professor. "Would you please hold on to this rail so that I can get my fare out?"

Read in the papers
An 18th century scientist Thomas Birch was a very keen fisherman, who, however, rarely caught anything. He approached the problem in a scientific manner and constructed an outfit which made him look like a tree. His arms fitted into the branches and he could see through holes in the bark.

Thus disguised, he set off down to the river bank and took up his position. The experiment could not be described as an exact success as he did not catch any fish, but stray dogs were grateful, as were the friends who used to picnic at his feet.

When pianist Arthur Rubinstein arrived in Moscow for a concert, he carefully searched his hotel room for listening devices.

Finding some wires under the carpet, he cut them with scissors.

Next morning a chambermaid told him of a curious occurence the night before. A chandelier had fallen down in the room beneath his.

A man wanted to have his house renovated, but thought that all the estimates he received were too high. Finally he consulted an Irish building contractor who came to view his house.

"I'll completely redecorate your bedroom for £ 15," said the Irishman.

"Great," said the man, "all the others wanted at least £ 100."

At this the Irishman rushed over to the window and shouted out "Green side up, green side up."

"How about the bathroom?", asked the man. "The others wanted at least £ 250."

"My men and I will do it for £ 38.57," said the Irishman, whereupon he rushed to the window and shouted "Green side up, green side up."

"Well you seem to be the man I've been looking for," said the man. "Just tell me one thing – why do you keep going to the window and shouting 'Green side up, green side up'?"

"That's just technical information to my workmen," said the Irishman. "They're laying a lawn next door."

Read in the papers
A Cornish scuba club decided to go diving in Loch Buidhe, Scotland.
After getting permission from the local laird, they drove 700 miles, brought all their equipment 3.000 feet up a mountain, and discovered that Loch Buidhe is only six inches deep.

Do you know why the idiot spent two weeks in a revolving door?
He couldn't find the doorhandle.

A friend found the absent-minded professor going round and round in a revolving door with a desperate look on his face.

"What's the trouble?" the friend called.

"I can't remember whether I'm on my way in or on my way out."

The absent-minded professor said to another professor, "I'd hardly recognize you. You've changed so much. You've put on a great deal of weight and your hair has turned grey and you don't wear glasses any longer. What has happened to you, Professor Dixon?"

"But I'm not Professor Dixon," came the answer.

"Remarkable. You've even changed your name."

Read in the papers
The San Diego, California branch of Mensa, the organisation for super-intelligent people, decided it would be fun to invite members of Densa, a group for those who reckon they're not so bright, to a wine and cheese party.
Densa president Jack Canaan said his members enjoyed it, but it would have been even better if the Mensa people had remembered the cheese.

What happened to the idiot who had a brain transplant?
The brain rejected him.

An idiot construction worker was going up and down the ladder with the same bricks each time.
"What's the idea?" asked one of his mates.
"Well," said the man, "I had an argument with the foreman and I'm fooling him. He thinks I'm working."

A man heard that 90 % of all accidents happen within a ten mile radius of your home. So he moved.

An old Irish woman was explaining to her neighbour that she didn't like teabags.
"By the time you've cut off all the corners and have taken the tea out, you'd have been better off buying a full half pound of tea in a packet in the first place."

Read in the papers
A shopper in a supermarket in Nuremberg, West Germany, collapsed at the checkout desk and was rushed to hospital. She had been trying to smuggle a frozen chicken out of the store under her hat.

A lady walked down the street carrying a small box that had holes punched in the top.
"What's in the box?" a friend asked.
"A cat," the lady answered.
"What for?"
"I've been dreaming about mice at night, and I'm frightened of mice. The cat is to catch them."
"But the mice you dream about are imaginary," said her friend.
The lady whispered, "So is the cat."

An idiot managed to get a job as a doorman in an office block. He did well with the PUSH and PULL signs. But he's still struggling with his fingers under a door marked LIFT!

In the bank one day Simple Simon suddenly called out at the top of his voice, "Has anybody dropped a wad of notes with a rubber band around it?"
Several people standing in the bank answered, "I have!"
"Well, I've just found the rubber band," said the simpleton.

Why did Simple Simon take hay to bed with him?
Because he wanted to feed his nightmare.

Read in the papers
A bank robber in Portland, Oregon, seemed to be somewhat lacking in confidence, when he decided to rob a bank in 1969. As he did not want to attract attention to himself, he wrote his instructions on a piece of paper, which he held up for the cashier to read. "This is a hold-up and I've got a gun" were the frightening words on the note.
The bemused bank official waited while the would-be bank robber wrote the next message and pushed it through the grille. This time the cashier read, "Put all the money in a paper bag."
After a moment's pause the cashier wrote on the bottom, "I don't have a paper bag," and passed it back. Apparently this was too much for the robber – he fled.

A man was digging a hole when his friend came along.
"What are you doing?" asked the friend.
"I'm digging a hole to bury my dog," was the reply.
"Well, what are the other holes for then?" asked the friend.
"Oh," said the first man. "They were going to be for the dog too, but they weren't big enough."

Sculptor: "Your brother's got a good head."
Tracey: "Good as new! Never been used."

A woman on the Underground noticed that the man sitting opposite her had a pigeon perched on each shoulder. He paid no attention as people crowded on and off at different stations. He just went on reading a newspaper.

Finally the woman got so curious that she spoke to the man. "Excuse me, sir, but would you mind telling me what those pigeons are doing on your shoulder?"

"I have no idea," the man answered. "They just got on at Oxford Circus."

Andrew: "Did you know we only use a third of our brains?"
Gary: "Really! What happens to the other third?"

Read in the papers

In 1972 Derek Langborne, a scientist from Upton, near Didcot, built a fire in his fireplace. After lighting it, he went outside to fill the coal box. On returning, he saw that a log had rolled out of the grate and set fire to the log box. He quickly picked it up and took it outside into the garden, but as he went out, he brushed against a curtain which covered the front door. A moment later both curtain and door were in flames.

As things were getting out of hand, Mr Langborne decided to phone the Fire Brigade. While telephoning he noticed that the burning log box in the garden had set fire to his car.

He quickly put on his overcoat and fetched a bucket of water to throw over the car. On his way, however, he fell over a partly-filled petrol can.

A neighbour who had been watching the scene called the fire brigade. By the time they arrived, Mr Langborne himself was on fire with flames now rising quickly from his overcoat.

Our nearest and dearest

Father: "What are you going to be when you've finished studying and passed all your exams?"
Son: "Probably an old age pensioner."

Alec: "Dad! Will you help me with my homework?"
Dad: "No son! That wouldn't be right, would it?"
Alec: "That doesn't matter, as long as it's done."

A twelve-year-old boy had to look after his sister while his parents went shopping. He decided to go fishing and took his sister along.
"I'll never do that again," said the boy to his parents.
"Why? Did she make a noise and frighten the fish away?"
"No," said the boy, "but she ate up all my worms!"

Read in the papers
Puzzled as to how to remove a particularly bad stain from his clothes, a Frenchman from Clermont-Ferand had a really bright idea. Instead of soap powder he put petrol in his washing machine. A spark from the motor ignited the petrol, which not only removed that hard-to-shift stain, but also the rest of the ground floor of his house.

"Dad, I'm just too tired to study tonight," said Jimmy.
"Now, my lad, hard work never killed anyone yet."
"So why should I run the risk of being the first?"

"The girl beside me in Maths is terribly clever," said
George to his mother. "She's clever enough for two."
"Perhaps you'd better think about marriage," said his
mother.

Small daughter: "Mummy, how many more days is it before Christmas?"
Mother: "Not many. Why do you ask?"
Small daughter: "I just wondered if it's near enough for
me to start being a good little girl."

Mum was the one in our family who made everybody behave. But once she was in hospital for a few days, and
Dad had to run the house. At dinner the first night little
Sally began to act like a spoilt brat.
"Sally, if you don't behave yourself, you'll have to go up
to your room," Dad said very severely.
Sally didn't look a bit frightened. Instead she just smiled
and said to her brother, "just listen to Daddy trying to talk
like Mum."

Father (at breakfast table): "That was some thunderstorm
we had last night, wasn't it, Freddy?"
Freddy: "It certainly was."
Mother: "Oh dear, why didn't you wake me up? You
know I can't sleep when there's thunder and lightning."

Alec: "Dad. I've just been expelled from school."

Dad: "WHAT!"

Alec: "Yes! It's taken me four years, but at last I've been expelled."

Father (on Coronation Day): "Where is Mother, Ted?"

Ted: "Upstairs, waving her hair."

Father: "Goodness! Can't we afford a flag?"

Grandma: "I like to go to bed and get up with the chickens, don't you?"

Susie: "No, I like to sleep in my own bed."

Johnny called up the stairs, "Mum, I tore a big hole in the seat of my trousers."

"Take them off and leave them by the sewing machine," his mother said. "Then come and get another pair."

Ten minutes went by, but Johnny did not come upstairs. His mother went down and saw the trousers by the sewing machine, but no sign of Johnny. Then she heard a rattling in the basement. So she called down the stairs, "Are you running round down there without any trousers on?"

"No, madam," a deep male voice answered. "I'm just reading the gas-meter."

An Eskimo mother was sitting in her igloo reading a bedtime story to her small son. "Little Jack Horner sat in a corner ..."

"Mum," interrupted the boy, "what's a corner?"

"Dad, were you good at running when you were at school?"

"Well I did once run the 100 yards in about 10 seconds."

"Gosh! That was fast."

"Yes. And if I ever find out who put the ants in my running shorts I'll hit him, even after all the years."

When Sally saw the tombstone with the inscription: "Here lies the body of a politician and an honest man" she wondered how they managed to get two people into the same grave.

For thirty years my mother-in-law and I were perfectly happy. Then we met.

"Mother, I think Grandma needs glasses."

"Why, son?"

"She's out in the kitchen looking at the washing machine."

"What's wrong with that?"

"Well, there are two pairs of father's long pants in it, and Grandma thinks she's seeing a wrestling match on television."

Mother was telling Father what a bad girl Susie had been. She had a fight with the boy next door. "It's all the fault of those terrible Jones children down the street," Mother concluded. "Susie learned about biting and hair-pulling from them."

At this point Susie interrupted, "That's right. But kicking on the shins was my own idea."

"Where do I come from, Mummy?" asked Alec.

"Oh, the stork brought you."

"Where does Daddy come from?" he went on.

"The fairies brought him," said Mum getting a bit nervous.

"And where did you come from, Mum?" Alec persisted.

"The gypsies brought me."

The next day in school where the biology master had been teaching Alec's class the facts of life, Alec said to the teacher: "Sir, remember you were telling us about childbirth yesterday."

"Yes Alec," said the teacher.

"Well it appears that there have been no cases of natural birth in my family for at least two generations."

An ill-informed father was showing his children around the Natural History Museum. They arrived at an exhibit of a stuffed flamingo.

Father: "This is the flamingo – now extinct."

Son: "But Dad, the flamingo isn't extinct."

Father: "Well, this one is!"

Little Julian had been carefully examining all the tombstones in the cemetery and reading all the various inscriptions when he suddenly asked his father: "Daddy, where do they bury all the horrible people?"

"Nick," his father asked angrily when he saw his son's school report, "why are you so awful at geography?"

"It's the teacher's fault, Dad. He keeps telling us about places I've never heard of."

Charles loved his elderly grandmother dearly and decided that for Christmas he would buy her a parrot as it would be someone for her to talk to and keep her company.

Charles went to a pet shop and insisted that the parrot had to have a large vocabulary and he ended up paying a thousand pounds for what the pet shop owner assured him was the most talkative parrot he'd ever seen.

Charles arranged for the parrot to be delivered to his grandmother on Christmas Eve and on Christmas Day he phoned his grandmother and asked: "How did you like the bird I sent you?"

"It was delicious!" she replied.

Father: "How's your arithmetic coming on, Mary?"
Mary: "Well I can cope with the noughts; it's the numbers I have a bit of trouble with."

What did ET's mother say to him when he finally got home?
"Where on earth have you been?"

Bright boy: "Dad, is your watch going?"
Dad: "Of course it is."
Bright boy: "Then when's it coming back?"

Sarah had told her daughter, three-year-old Fiona, to be on her best behaviour when she visited one of her aunts who was a stickler for good manners.

"Always say 'please' and 'thank you'," cautioned Sarah. "And whatever you do, always be polite."

So at lunch when the aunt asked Fiona, "Can you manage your meat? Or would you like me to cut it in small pieces for you?" Fiona replied: "No, thank you. I can manage on my own, thank you. We sometimes have meat as tough as this at home.

Read in the papers
Mrs Janet Trent, of Paddington, London, opened her diary one morning to check her day's schedule and found the entry: "House burgled 5 a.m."

Saints and sinners

Father Clancy rang up the local council to ask that a dead goat be removed from in front of his house. The clerk who took the call thought he'd be smart:
"I thought you priests took care of the dead," he said.
"We do," said Father Clancy. "But first we have to get in touch with the relatives."

It was the little English girl's first visit to a church in the USA.
The clergyman was an extremely energetic preacher and during his sermon he stood in the pulpit and gesticulated wildly with his hands, shouted at his congregation, hitting on the sides of the pulpit with his fists to emphasize certain points, and his facial expressions ranged from rage to kindness showing great passion.
As the clergyman stamped his feet and banged on his pulpit again, the little girl turned to her mother and whispered: "I hope they keep him locked up in that little box – I wouldn't like to be near him if he gets out."

When little Cathy went to mass for the first time she was fascinated. She peered around in all directions and then tugged her father's sleeve.
"Where's God, Daddy?"
Her father pointed towards the altar. Just then the sanctus bells rang. Another tug.
"Shouldn't He answer His phone?"

Young Michael Mahoney was attending mass for the first time, and he couldn't take his eyes off the choir-boys, all in their white clothes. At last he whispered to his father:
"Daddy, are they all going to have their hair cut?"

A Catholic family and a Protestant family shared a holiday house at the coast. The weather was warm and there was nobody else at the beach so the parents let the little Catholic boy and Protestant girl, both aged five, swim without any costumes. When they came out of the water they were asked:
"Did you enjoy your swim?"
"Yes we did, thank you. And not only that. Now we know what the difference is between a Catholic and a Protestant."

Some people hate to be left out of anything. A note published by the Vatican stated that there are now 143 officially recognized sins. They have received thousands of letters from all over the world asking for a copy of the complete list.

An Irishman who was rather too fond of strong drink was asked by the parish priest: "My son, how do you expect to get into heaven?"

The Irishman replied:

"Sure, and that's easy! When I get to the gates of Heaven I'll open the door, and shut the door, and open the door and shut the door, and keep on doing that till St. Peter gets impatient and says, "For goodness' sake, Mike, either come in or stay out!"

There was heavy knocking on the Pearly Gates one day.

"Who's there?" called St. Peter.

"It is I," said the voice.

"Oh God," sighed the saint. "Not another clever English teacher."

During mass the young boy was very restless and his dad had a lot of trouble keeping him still. The lad was fascinated by the red sanctuary lamp and, after a time, he clutched his father's arm. "Dad! Dad! When it turns green can we go?"

The priest was sitting one afternoon in the sacristy of his church, just behind the statue of Mary, when one of the little girls from the parish primary school came into the church and approached the statue.

"Dear Our Lady. Can I bring my friend Cheryl to the parish picnic next month? She's not a Catholic."

The priest heard this.

"She can't come," he said in a deep voice.

At which the girl angrily responded:

"You keep quiet God. I'm talking to your Mother."

Father Conaghan had been in the parish for five years and now he was leaving to go to another parish. The send-off celebration took the form of a huge barbecue to which most of the parish came.

During the afternoon one of the older ladies came to Father Conaghan:

"I don't know how we'll ever do without you. Until you came we didn't know what sin was."

Watching her young son busy drawing, his mother asked:

"What are you drawing, darling?"

"I'm drawing God."

"But nobody knows what God looks like."

"They will when I've finished drawing."

Read in the papers
Investigating a report that a busload of fully robed Ku Klux Klansmen had been seen driving through a racially mixed district of Gloucester, police discovered it was a coach carrying monks from a nearby abbey to the town's cathedral.

Because of a poor potato crop in Cambridgeshire, a packet of instant mash was displayed at the altar at Rampton for Harvest Thanksgiving.

To escape from the worries of everyday life, William joined a religious order where all the members took a vow of silence. On only one day each year were the members allowed to speak, and then they could each say only two words.

After he had been in the order for a year, Brother William was brought to the Abbot's study.

"You are permitted to say two words only. Do you understand?"

Brother William nodded.

"Do you wish to speak?"

He nodded again.

"Then what are your two words?"

"More food."

Another year went by and again he was brought to the Abbot's study.

"Do you wish to speak?"

Nod.

"What are your two words?"

"More blankets."

The third year went by and he was brought to the Abbot
again.

"Do you wish to speak?"

Nod.

"What are your two words?"

"I quit."

"It's a good thing too," said the Abbot. "You've done
nothing but complain ever since you got here."

A bishop was giving a talk to Alec's class. "When I was at boarding school," he said, "I shared a room with eleven other boys, but I was the only one who got down on my knees and prayed every night. Can anyone think of anything braver than that?"

"Yes!" said Alec."Imagine a room with eleven bishops in it, and being the only one not to kneel down and pray every night."

When the Pope died he went to heaven and was given very comfortable but not particularly grand lodgings.

Three days later a school-teacher died and when he arrived he was given a luxurious palace.

The Pope heard about this and complained to Saint Peter. "I was Pope after all and he was just a school master. He's got a palace and I've got a small apartment."

"Listen Your Holiness," said Saint Peter. "You're the 150th Pope we've had in here. He's the first school-teacher."

Behind the inn at Bethlehem the shepherds found the stable where the new-born child who was to be the hope of Israel lay. They opened the creaking door and saw the holy family in the lamplight for the first time. Joseph called softly to them.

"Come inside."

The floor was covered with straw and none of the men saw the rake that was lying in it with its prongs upward. One of them stepped on it and the handle flew up and dealt him a cruel blow on the forehead.

"Jesus Christ!" he exclaimed.

"Now that's a good idea," said Joseph. "We were thinking of calling Him Fred."

Traveller's joy

Once there were three men travelling in an aeroplane.
Unfortunately, one fell out.
Fortunately, there was a haystack below him.
Unfortunately, there was a pitchfork in the haystack.
Fortunately, he missed the pitchfork.
Unfortunately, he missed the haystack.

Read in the papers
The quiet American transcontinental jet flight was disturbed in 1976 by a passenger who called one of the air stewardesses and demanded: "Take this plane to Detroit." When it was explained to him that the plane was already going to Detroit, he sat down again.

Derek Mayhew was the only passenger on a British Airways jumbo jet flight from the Arabian Gulf to London, with only one suitcase. When he got to Heathrow it was missing. It turned up three days later.

Sally: "How did you find the weather on holiday?"
Debbie: "I just went outside and there it was."

The weather was terrible for the whole two weeks of my holiday. I didn't get brown from the sun, but from the rust caused by the rain.

Then there was the tourist in a little Sligo village who noticed that the two clocks on the church showed different times.
He asked a local to explain.
"Look," said the Sligoman, "if both clocks showed the same time, we would need only one clock."

Mr Smith: "Do you have a room for tonight?"
Hotel receptionist: "Do you have a reservation?"
Mr Smith: "No. I'm not a Red Indian."

Resident of Barbados: "In Barbados we always have fantastic weather."
Visiting English woman: "Then how on earth do you start a conversation with a stranger?"

"This holiday", announced Susie, "has made me feel very religious."

"Good heavens Susie, why is that?" asked her surprised parents.

"Because," she replied, "I didn't believe in hell until we got here!"

Read in the papers
A couple away from home on holiday in 1971 took a 'mystery' tour by rail – and ended up back in their home town of Margate, Kent.

Read in the papers

The voyage from Belfast to Plymouth, which normally takes a few days, proved to be a long trip for Mr Ronald Davies.

Mr Davies was suspected by the UDA Protestants of working for the IRA. He was also suspected by the IRA of working for British Intelligence. So in 1974 he decided to get away from this impossible situation and, accompanied by his girlfriend Brenda Collopy, set sail for the Isle of Man in their sailing ship. On the way over they got lost and had to be guided into Douglas by a lifeboat. They made their way to Holyhead and set off again – this time in the direction of Fishguard. When they failed to arrive, the coastguards started a search. The two travellers eventually arrived back in Ireland at Waterford. Once again they set course for Fishguard, but turned up back in Holyhead and it was only on the 3rd attempt that they managed to make the trip.

The adventures continued when later, off the Devon coast, they had to be guided into Clovelly. In Cornish waters, their first port was Padstowe and from here they set off for Newquay, but had to return after being caught in a storm and rescued by the Padstowe lifeboat. Miss Callopy had apparently had more than she could stand and left the boat.

Five weeks later Mr Davies was again rescued by the Padstowe lifeboat just off St. Ives. In August 1977 he completed the journey overland. The whole trip had taken just over two years, had caused six coastguard alarms, four lifeboat rescues and the assistance of a Royal Navy helicopter and the aircraft carrier *Hermes*.

What's brown, hairy and wears sunglasses?
A coconut on holiday.

Pat: "Er, is that British Airways? Can you tell me how long it takes to fly from Dublin to London?"
Booking clerk: "Just a minute, sir..."
Pat: "O.K. Thanks a lot," and he hung up.

Read in the papers

Probably one of the strangest tales of tourism is the one about Mr Nicholas Scotti of San Francisco, who, in 1977, decided to fly back from America to his birthplace in Italy to visit relatives.

The plane made a one-hour fuel stop at Kennedy Airport. Mr Scotti, believing himself to have arrived in Italy, got out and spent two days in New York without realizing that he was not in Rome.

When his nephews were not there to meet him, Mr Scotti thought that it was due to the heavy Roman traffic mentioned in their letters. He noticed that many, if not all, of the famous landmarks had been replaced by modern buildings.

Another strange fact was that many people spoke English with an American accent – but this only confirmed Mr Scotti's opinion that Americans were everywhere. Furthermore he thought that it was for their benefit that the street signs were written in English.

Mr Scotti, who spoke very little English himself, asked a policeman (in Italian) the way to the bus de-pot. By the greatest coincidence the policeman came from Naples and answered in fluent Italian.

He was finally handed over to another policeman after he had travelled round twelve hours on a bus. Mr Scotti was astonished to find that the Rome po-lice force employed people who could not even speak Italian and there was a short argument.

Finally an interpreter was called and even then Mr Scotti refused to believe it when he was told that he was in New York. His opinion seemed to be con-firmed when he was raced to the airport in a police car with screaming sirens so that he could catch the plane back to San Francisco. Mr Scotti told his interpreter, "I know I'm in Italy – that's how they drive."

A woman passenger travelling first-class had been calling for the steward every few minutes on the Gulf Air London-Bahrein flight.
Then, when her baby had filled its nappy, she handed the child to him, ordering: "Change it."
The steward obliged by placing a similar baby from tourist class in her lap and asking: "Will this one do?"
He was severely reprimanded after both mothers complained.

Did you hear about the man who paid £ 10 for a sheet of sandpaper?
He thought it was a map of the Sahara Desert.

"So you're not going to Berlin this year?"
"No, it's Rome we're not going to. It was Berlin we didn't go to last year."

Some people are terrified of flying. Take poor old Royston, who wanted to go to Spain for his summer holiday; nothing would induce him to go on a plane so he had to travel by boat and train. But he was right out of luck – his train crashed. A plane fell on it ...

The train was crawling slowly across country from Dublin to Ballinasloe, and the English tourist was growing increasingly impatient. Finally he jumped out at one of the many stops, walked along to the engine-driver and said, "Can't you go any faster, driver?"

"Sure I can," replied the driver, "but I'm not allowed to leave the train."

Tommy: "I had a rotten holiday this year!"
Fred: "Why's that, then?"
Tommy: "The weather was lousy. We went to the zoo, but all we saw was the keeper building an ark."

"I tried surf-riding while I was in Australia."
"How did you get on?"
"Not very well, I couldn't get the horse near the water."

"I hear you've just come back from India."
"That's right – I was the guest of a rajah."
"Were you really? Did you go hunting?"
"Oh yes. One day he took me into the jungle to shoot tigers."
"Any luck?"
"Yes – we didn't meet any!"

"I have learnt some white man's magic," said the African Chief on returning to his country after a brief stay in England.
"What?" asked his brother.
"First, you must make a smooth piece of ground and get grass to grow on it. Then you carefully tend the grass. Af-

118

ter that you place some sticks in the grass and get some men to put on all-white clothes. Two of the men have to carry pieces of wood called 'bats' and another man has to carry a red ball. After a bit of running about between the sticks by two of the men and some throwing of the red ball, it will rain."

Vocabulary

A

abandon (v.) [ə'bændən]
: – give up or finish s.th. without the intended result

ant (n.) [ænt]
: – small insect, living in large social groups on the ground, known for working hard

astray (adv.) [ə'strei]
: – away from the right way or path

B

bagpipes (n.) ['bægpaips]
: – musical instrument with air stored in a bag and forced out through pipes, played esp. in Scotland

bargain (n.) ['ba:gin]
: – here: article sold at a low price

bleep (v.) [bli:p]
: – highpitched signals or sounds sent out as a warning

boast (v.) [bəust]
: – talk with pride (often used in a negative sense)

bonnet (n.) ['bɔnit]
: – the cover over the engine of a car

boot (n.) [bu:t]
: – here: place for luggage at the back of a car

brat (n.) [bræt]
: – child, esp. a bad mannered one

breed (v.) [bri:d]
: – keep animals to produce young animals, esp. by selection (used also for plants)

bump into old friends [bʌmp]
: – meet them by chance

burgle (v.) [bə:gl]
: – break into a house and steal s.th.

burst at the seams
: – be extremely full

C

canary (n.) [kə'nɛəri]
: – small yellow bird kept as a pet for its beautiful song

120

castor-oil (n.) ['ka:stər'ɔil]	– thick yellowish oil used as medicine, causing the bowels to empty easily
chambermaid (n.) ['tʃeimbəmeid]	– girl or woman in a hotel who keeps the bedrooms tidy
chandelier (n.) [ˌʃændi'liə]	– large hanging decorative holder for candles or electric lights
chisel (n.) ['tʃizl]	– metal tool with a cutting edge at one end
conker (n.) ['kɔŋkə]	– the brown, shiny seed of the chestnut tree
cox (n.) [kɔks]	– person who controls and guides the crew of a rowing boat
current events ['kʌrənt i'vents]	– affairs, events of the day or present time
curse (n.) [kəːs]	– phrase or word spoken to make s. th. harmful or evil happen to s. th. or s. o.

D

desperate (adj.) ['despərit]	– prepared to do anything, esp. because of loss of hope
devotion (n.) [di'vəuʃən]	– great loyalty or fondness
dizzy (adj.) ['dizi]	– feeling as if things are going round and round
donor (n.) ['dəunə]	– person who gives s. th., esp. for a good purpose
dose (n.) [dəus]	– measured amount of a medicine
drone (v.) [drəun]	– speak with a monotonous, low voice
dumb (adj.) [dʌm]	– here: stupid ('Play the ~ blonde in a film')
dye (v.) [dai]	– change the colour of s. th. (e.g. hair, clothes) by dipping it into a liquid

E

estimate (n.) ['estimit]	– approximate calculation of size, value, etc.
exceptional (adj.) [ik'sepʃənl]	– unusual
expel (v.) [iks'pel]	– exclude, dismiss officially

extinct (adj.) [iks'tiŋkt] – a species of animal (e.g. dinosaurs) which has died out

F

familiar (adj.) [fə'miljə] – here: too friendly, showing lack of respect

fiancé (n.) [fi'ãːnsei] – (fem.: fiancée) the person one is going to marry and to whom one is engaged

G

gamekeeper (n.) ['geim'kiːpə] – man who takes care of animals such as pheasants or deer, kept on a country estate

geese (n.) [giːs] – (pl. of 'goose') birds that look almost like ducks but larger; we like to eat them at Christmas

goat (n.) [gəut] – horned animals, which provide wool and milk, related to the sheep, can eat almost anything

gooseberry (n.) ['guzbəri] – small round green fruit which grows on a bush, and often tastes a little sour

GPO – abbreviation for: General Post Office

grate (n.) [greit] – metal frame that holds the wood or coal in a fireplace

H

halo (n.) ['heiləu] – circle of light or golden ring around the head of holy people

horseshoe (n.) ['hɔːsʃuː] – U-shaped piece of iron nailed under a horse's foot

hubcap (n.) ['hʌbkæp] – metal covering over the centre of a car wheel

hypochondriac (n.) [‚haipəu'kɔndriæk] – person who is always unnecessarily worried about his/her health

I

ignite (v.) [ig'nait] – set on fire

induce (v.) [in'djuːs] – persuade s.o. to do s.th.

inevitable (adj.) [in'evitəbl] – which cannot be avoided; certain to happen

inscription (n.) [in'skripʃən] – writing on stone

interfere (v.) [ˌintə'fiə] – take part in a matter that does not concern one

J

jack (n.) [dʒæk] – here: tool for lifting a car when changing tyres

join s.o. in a drink – have a drink with s.o.

jurisdiction (n.) [ˌdʒuəris'dikʃən] – legal authority and the right to exercise this

juror (n.) ['dʒuərə] – member of a jury

L

landing (n.) ['lændiŋ] – 1. platform at the top of a set of stairs 2. act of arriving and bringing s.th. (e.g. a plane) to land

landmark (n.) ['lændmaːk] – here: object, building, etc. which is easily seen from a distance and helpful to travellers

licence plate (n.) ['laisəns pleit] – number-plate of a car

limp (v.) [limp] – walk with one foot or leg moving less well than the other

log (n.) [lɔg] – thick piece of wood

lose one's looks – change of appearance which is for the worse

M

maggot (n.) ['mægət] – tiny wormlike creature, found on food, where flies have laid their eggs

mare (n.) [mɛə] – female horse

mass (n.) [mæs] – ceremony in Catholic and Orthodox churches

mate (n.) [meit] – friend

midwife (n.) ['midwaif] – woman educated to help women in childbirth miser (n.) ['maizə]   – person who loves money for its own sake and spends as little as possible

mule (n.) [mjuːl]   – animal that is the offspring of a male donkey and a female horse

N

nap, take a ~ [næp]   – have a short sleep, esp. during daytime

nativity play (n.) [nə'tiviti 'plei]   – play (performed by children at school) telling the story of the birth of Christ

nightmare (n.) ['naitmɛə]   – terrible dream

nitrogen (n.) ['naitrədʒən]   – gas without smell, taste or colour; forms about four-fifths of the atmosphere (symbol N)

O

oarsman (n.) ['ɔːzmən]   – man who rows a boat, esp. in races

off-licence (n.) ['ɔf'laisəns]   – shop where bottles of alcoholic drinks are sold to be taken away

offhand (adj.) ['ɔf'hænd]   – here: without having time to think or prepare; at once

oxygen (n.) ['ɔksidʒən]   – gas without smell, taste or colour; present in the air; necessary for all forms of life on Earth (symbol O)

P

parachute ['pærəʃuːt]   – 1.(n.): when jumping from an aeroplane you need a ~ to come down to earth safely
2.(v.): drop from an aeroplane by means of a ~

parrot (n.) ['pærət]   – tropical bird, often gaily coloured, often has ability to imitate the human voice

pavilion (n.) [pə'viljən]   – here: building beside a cricket field for the players and those watching the game

pedestrian precinct [pə'destrïən 'priːsiŋkt]	– area in cities where traffic is not allowed
perch (v.) [pəːtʃ]	– (of bird) come to rest somewhere
pierce (v.) [piəs]	– make a hole with a sharp-pointed instrument
pigeon (n.) ['pidʒin]	– bird (wild or tame) of the dove family; a carrier ~ is trained to carry messages
pitchfork (n.) ['pitʃfɔːk]	– farm tool with two long metal points used for lifting and throwing hay and straw
pregnant (adj.) ['pregnənt]	– carrying an unborn child
prescription (n.) [pri'skripʃən]	– here: written order by a doctor for particular medicine or treatment
prosecute (v.) ['prɔsikjuːt]	– start legal proceedings against s.o.
pulpit (n.) ['pulpit]	– raised enclosed structure in a church used by the priest when preaching
pylon (n.) ['pailən]	– here: steel framework for supporting cables that carry electricity over land

R

raisin (n.) ['reizn]	– dried grape, used for cakes, etc.
rake (n.) [reik]	– gardening tool with a row of points (prongs) at the end, mainly used for levelling the soil
rascal (n.) ['raːskəl]	– dishonest person
reel (n.) [riːl]	– cylinder or s.th. similar on which wire, film, etc. can be wound
reindeer (n.) ['reindiə]	– large kind of deer used in Lapland to draw sledges across the snow
remedy (n.) ['remidi]	– method of curing a disease
reprimand (v.) [repri'maːnd]	– disapprove officially
revolving door (n.) [ri'vɔlviŋ 'dɔə]	– door that goes round in a circle
roam the pasture [rəum ðə'paːstʃə]	– wander across grassy land

rodent (n.) ['rəʊdənt]   – small animal (e.g. rat, mouse, squirrel) with strong sharp front teeth

rude (adj.) [ruːd]   – bad-mannered, very impolite

run a risk   – take a risk

S

salmon (n.) ['sæmən]   – fish with pink flesh; swims up rivers to lay its eggs

schedule (n.) ['ʃedjuːl]   – list of things to be done

scrap (v.) [skræp]   – here: get rid of or throw away as useless

scuba (n.) ['skuːbə]   – instrument for breathing while swimming under water

sermon (n.) ['səːmən]   – part of a Christian church service, a talk usually based on a sentence from the Bible

shed (v.) [ʃed]   – here: fall out or come off naturally

shin (n.) [ʃin]   – front part of the leg between knee and ankle

short cut (n.)   – quicker more direct way than the ordinary way

show off (v.)   – try to impress people by talking about one's wealth, abilities, etc.

shut up (v.)   – 1. close; 2. be or make quiet (colloquial)

sink (n.) [siŋk]   – basin in a kitchen, where you do the washing-up, etc.

soap opera (n.) [səʊp 'ɔpərə] – radio or television serial, usually about the daily life and problems of the characters

spark (n.) [spaːk]   – small piece of burning material

spend late nights   – go to bed very late

stain (n.) [stein]   – marked or discoloured spot

stationery (n.) ['steiʃnəri] – all the materials you need for writing (pencils, paper, etc.)

stickler (n.) ['stiklə]   – person who thinks a particular type of behaviour to be very important

straw, the last ~ [strɔː] – an addition to a problem or troubles that makes it/them unbearable superstitious (adj.) [ˌsjuːpəˈstiʃəs] – people who believe that eg. the number 13 brings bad luck are ~

surgical spirit (n.) [ˈsəːdʒikəl ˈspirit] – medical alcohol used for cleaning wounds

T

temper (n.) [ˈtempə] – a person's state of mind; try to keep one's ~: try not to become angry

tombstone (n.) [ˈtuːm-stəun] – stone on a grave

tortoise (n.) [ˈtɔːtəs] – four-legged land animal with body covered by a hard shell

track down (v.) [træk] – find s. th. by searching and following tracks

trespass (v.) [ˈtrespəs] – enter private property without permission

tune, out of ~ [tjuːn] – not at the correct musical pitch

turf (n.) [təːf] – squares of soil with a thick covering of grass

turn a cow into a field – put a cow into a field so that it can eat the grass

turpentine (n.) [ˈtəːpəntain] – thin oil often used to make paint thinner

U

unbearable (adj.) [ʌnˈbɛərəbl] – too unpleasant or bad to be accepted; intolerable

undertaker (n.) [ˈʌndəˌteikə] – a person who prepares the dead for their funeral

V

vain (adj.) [vein] – full of self-admiration

virgin (n.) [ˈvəːdʒin] – a person who has never had sex

vow of silence [vau] – promise to God that one will not speak

W

wad (n.) [wɔd] — pieces of paper fastened together

wave (v.) [weiv] — 1. move s. th. as a signal (e. g. a flag or one's hand)
2. curl one's hair

woodpecker (n.) ['wud,pekə] — bird which can make holes in trees with its beak

wrestling (n.) ['resliŋ] — sport in which you try to hold or throw your opponent onto the ground

Y

yeast (n.) [jiːst] — substance used to make bread and cakes rise and for producing alcohol in wine and beer

Bildnachweis

Seite 2, 11, 23, 30, 45, 47, 49, 61, 67, 71, 77, 89, 93, 97, 99, 107, 113, 119: aus "Picture Jokes For Kids"
Seite 15, 17, 31, 63, 73, 115: aus "The Great Big Joke Book For Kids"
Seite 25, 33, 37, 56, 81, 102: aus "The Biggest Joke and Puzzle Book For Kids"
Die genannten Titel sind bei Ward Lock LTD, London, erschienen. Wir danken World International Publishers LTD, Manchester, für die freundliche Abdruckgenehmigung.

Seite 84: aus "A–Z of Animal Jokes" von Scoular Anderson. Der genannte Titel ist bei Young Corgi Books, London, erschienen. Wir danken Transworld Publishers LTD, London, für die freundliche Abdruckgenehmigung.

Seite 109: aus "Money is Funny" von Joel Rothman. Dieser Titel ist bei Fontana Books, London, erschienen. Wir danken Collins Publishers, London, für die freundliche Abdruckgenehmigung.